THE
NIGHT SKY

This I-SPY book belongs to:_____

To appreciate the sky and stars in their full glory you need to find the best possible conditions, preferably somewhere really dark, maybe at the bottom of your garden. You will get good views during long winter nights but, if you live in a town, the glare from the lights may make it difficult to see very faint stars. You can see most when you are in the country or at the seaside so try watching the stars when you are on holiday. There are three things you should remember: Always tell your parents if you want to watch the stars. Astronomy is a good excuse for staying up late! Try to get them or an elder brother or sister to come with you.

Always wear warm clothes. Even in the summer, it is sometimes very cold at night. And, if you shiver, it wobbles your binoculars or telescope! Because you are out in the dark, you need a torch to see your book. A bright light dazzles your eyes, so cover the end of the torch with red tissue paper or red plastic film to give a dim red light. After you have been outside for a while you will find you can see much more than at first.

After you have been outside for a while you will find you can see much more than at first as your eyes become more accustomed to the dark.

How to use your I-SPY book

You will need 1000 points to send off for your I-SPY certificate (see page 64) but that is not too difficult because there are masses of points in every book. As you make each I-SPY, write your score in the box and where there is a question, check your answer against the correct one on page 63.

The Moon Illusion

When the Moon (especially the Full Moon) is low on the horizon it appears enormous. In fact, it is actually exactly the same size as when it is high in the sky. This is known as the 'Moon Illusion' – your brain simply thinks it is bigger when compared with distant hills or buildings. Test it for yourself: hold a finger at arm's length and you will see that it is about twice the width of the Moon, wherever the Moon is in the sky. Actually, the same effect occurs with the Sun, but remember you must never look at the Sun through binoculars or any telescope because of the danger of damaging your eyes.

😃 I-SPY Tick List:

- **The moon low on the horizon**   10 ◯

- **The moon high in the sky**   10 ◯

VISIT A PLANETARIUM

A good way of learning about the sky is to visit a **planetarium**, where a special projector shows the night sky on the inside of a dome. At least there it is warm, so you can learn the sky in comfort!

Greenwich Planetarium

LEARN STARS IN A PLANETARIUM

Planetariums have many different programmes about the planets, galaxies and black holes, for example. Try to attend a programme about how to find your way around the sky and learning the different constellations.

 I-SPY Tick List:

- **Planetarium – Double if you visit one**   10 ◯
- **Learn the stars**   10 ◯
- **Planisphere – Double if you have one**   10 ◯

PLANISPHERE
LATITUDE 51.5° NORTH
Northern Europe, Northern USA
and Canada

SHOWS THE POSITIONS OF THE STARS AND CONSTELLATIONS FOR ANY HOUR IN THE YEAR

USE A PLANISPHERE

Another good way of finding out which star can be seen, and at what times, is to use a **planisphere**. This is a special map of the sky, marked so that you can set it to any date and time. It then shows exactly what you will be able to see.

With the naked eye you can see about 8,500 stars over the whole sky.

BINOCULARS

You don't have to have a telescope to look at the night sky. You can see lots of things with just your eyes. If you can, borrow a pair of **binoculars**. They are often much better even than big telescopes in helping you to see things in the sky and are easier to use.

REFRACTING TELESCOPE

Amateur astronomers use various types of telescopes. One, known as a **refractor**, uses lenses at each end of a tube. (The large one where the light enters is known as the objective, and the smaller one, which is adjustable so everything looks sharp, is called the eyepiece.) You look straight through the telescope at the sky.

REFLECTING TELESCOPE

Another type of telescope, known as a **reflector**, uses mirrors instead of lenses (as well as an eyepiece), and you have to look in the side of the tube. The mirrors act as a magnifier to enlarge the subject.

 I-SPY Tick List:

• **Binoculars**	10 ○
• **Refracting telescope**	10 ○
• **Reflecting telescope**	10 ○
• **Schmidt-Cassegrain** telescope	10 ○

SCHMIDT-CASSEGRAIN TELESCOPE

Some telescopes use both lenses and mirrors. They are popular with amateur astronomers because they are easy to carry from place to place. One type you may see is called a **Schmidt-Cassegrain**, named after two astronomers who designed telescopes.

HOW THE SKY ROTATES

Although the stars are actually scattered about in space they look as if they are on the inside of a giant dome. When you stand outside – like the little figure in the diagram (below) – the stars are overhead and the horizon is all around you.

Just as the Sun moves across the sky during the day, so the stars move during the night, because the Earth itself is rotating.

One star, called **Polaris**, appears to stand still at the North Pole of the sky, and all the other stars seem to rotate around it.

Only in a photograph, such as the one shown here (right), can you see that Polaris is not quite at the North Pole. The exposure needed for the photograph was several hours, and all the stars have left trails as the sky moved. The very short, bright trail near the centre was made by Polaris.

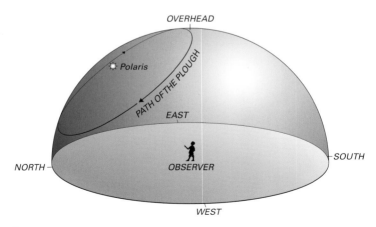

Northern sky and Polaris

What is another name for Polaris?

10 points for the correct answer.

 I-SPY Tick List:

• **Plough**	10	◯
• **Polaris**	10	◯

Plough

FIND THE PLOUGH AND POLARIS

How do you find Polaris? First you find a well-known group of seven stars known as the **Plough** (or **Dipper** in North America), with an easily remembered shape, rather like a saucepan with a long handle. Because they are very close to the North Pole, the stars of the Plough never dip below the horizon. The two end stars of the Plough are called the Pointers, because a line through them points to Polaris.

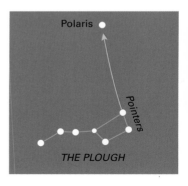

10

PICTURES IN THE SKY

Because the Earth revolves around the Sun once a year, the Sun appears to move slowly across the sky, hiding different stars during the daytime as the months go by. So the stars that you see at night also change with the time of the year. Later in this book you can see what the sky looks like at four different seasons.

How many constellations cover the whole sky?

10 points for the correct answer.

To help them find their way around the sky at different times of the year, earlier pioneers invented names for various groups of stars, or **constellations**. Astronomers use the Latin names for constellations in modern sky atlases, so everyone, anywhere on Earth, knows which groups of stars they are talking about.

Cassiopeia

🙂 **I-SPY Tick List:**

• **Old book of constellations**	10 ○	
• **Modern star atlas**	10 ○	

11

THE NAMES OF STARS

Most bright stars have individual names, and many of these come from Arabic words that described their positions in the imaginary constellation patterns on the sky. The red star at the northeast (top left) of **Orion**, for example, is known as Betelgeuse, which probably means 'the woman in the middle'. (The Arabs saw the constellation as a woman.) The brilliant bluish star at the southeastern (bottom right) corner is Rigel, meaning 'foot'.

The name Polaris in Ursa Major, however, comes from Latin.

Orion

What is the English name for Orion?

10 points for the correct answer.

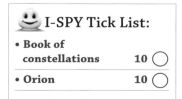

😊 **I-SPY Tick List:**

• **Book of constellations**	**10** ◯
• **Orion**	**10** ◯

Rising and Setting Stars

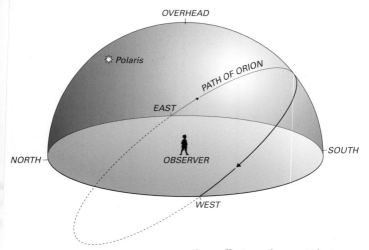

OVERHEAD

Polaris

PATH OF ORION

EAST

OBSERVER

NORTH

SOUTH

WEST

Constellations close to Polaris (mainly those shown on the chart on page 25) always remain above the horizon. (They are known as 'circumpolar constellations'.) Many other constellations are farther away from Polaris and the North Pole, so they rise and set during the night. The diagram shows how the constellation called Orion (page 36) rises above the horizon in the east, becomes highest in the south, and then disappears as it sets in the west.

Venus, Jupiter and the Moon

 There are at least 5 known dwarf planets, the largest of which, Eris, is about 2,300-2,400 kilometres in diameter, and orbits way beyond Neptune.

 Smaller than planets and dwarf planets, there are hundreds of thousands of known asteroids in the Solar System, from Pallas (about 550km across) down to tiny rocks just a few metres in size.

WATCHING PLANETS

Stars shine because they are extremely hot and give out their own light. The Moon and **planets**, on the other hand, only reflect light from the Sun. Two planets, **Venus** and **Jupiter**, shine like very bright stars, and two others, **Mars** and **Saturn**, although fainter, are also sometimes easy to see. All these planets (and the other, fainter ones) orbit the Sun just like the Earth.

Movements of Jupiter and Saturn in 2000

JUPITER'S SATELLITES

Jupiter has four large **satellites** in orbit around it (three are larger than our Moon). They are easily seen through binoculars, appearing on each side of the planet.

Who first saw Jupiter's satellites through a telescope?

10 points for the correct answer.

MOVEMENTS OF THE PLANETS

Because they are orbiting the Sun, planets do not have fixed positions like the stars, so they cannot be drawn on the maps here. You can sometimes find details of where they are in the newspapers and also on the Internet. Venus is always close to the Sun, so it is in the west in the evening, and in the east early in the morning. The picture shows the movement of Jupiter (the bright planet) and Saturn near the Pleiades cluster (page 32) over several months.

😊 I-SPY Tick List:

• **Venus in the evening**	10 ◯
• **Venus in the morning**	10 ◯
• **Jupiter**	10 ◯
• **Jupiter's satellites**	20 ◯
• **Mars**	20 ◯
• **Saturn** (a yellowish colour)	20 ◯

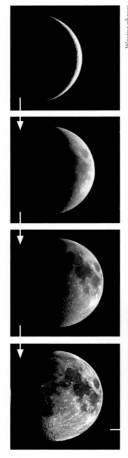

Waxing phases

THE PHASES OF THE MOON

As the Moon goes around the Earth, we see it by the light from the Sun that it reflects. It always turns the same side towards us, so sometimes it is in darkness, sometimes partly lit, and sometimes a complete, bright circle.

At **New Moon** the disk is completely dark, but a very thin, young crescent that appears in the western sky shortly after sunset is often called by the same name. The ends of the crescent (the horns) are turned towards the east.

As the days go by, the Moon appears farther towards the east at sunset, and the bright area waxes (increases). When half of the Moon can be seen, it is called **First Quarter**.

Full moon

16

The bright area continues to increase, until the whole face of the Moon is shining at **Full Moon**. Between First Quarter and Full Moon, the Moon is called **waxing gibbous**.

After Full Moon the bright area begins to wane (decrease), first through **waning gibbous**, then **Last Quarter**, and finally to **waning crescent**, until it disappears close to the Sun in the east at sunrise.

😊 I-SPY Tick List:

• Narrow crescent moon (New Moon)	10	◯
• The horns of the crescent	10	◯
• First Quarter	10	◯
• Waxing gibbous	10	◯
• Full moon	10	◯
• Waning gibbous	10	◯
• Last Quarter	10	◯
• Waning crescent	10	◯

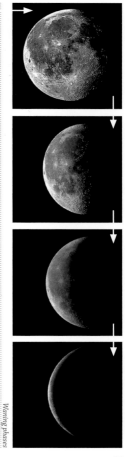

Waning phases

17

EARTHSHINE

Sometimes when the Moon appears as a crescent, you can see the rest of it, faintly illuminated by sunshine that has been reflected from the Earth on to the dark part of the Moon. This is called **Earthshine**.

LUNAR SEAS AND HIGHLANDS

Some parts of the Moon's surface are darker than others. These dark grey areas are called **maria** (Latin for 'seas'). They are flat lava plains. Most of the Apollo missions to the Moon landed in the maria, because they were safer and more predictable that the more rugged areas.

The lighter areas are called the **highlands**, and they contain nearly all the craters that pock-mark the face of the Moon. One Apollo mission, Apollo 17, landed on the edge of the highlands. At Full Moon, some craters show bright rays where powdered rock has been splashed out by the impacts. The longest rays belong to a crater called Tycho.

 Moon Landings
Only six NASA space missions have landed on the surface of the moon:

Apollo 11 – 16 July 1969
Apollo 12 – 14 November 1969
Apollo 14 – 31 January 1971
Apollo 15 – 26 July 1971
Apollo 16 – 16 April 1972
Apollo 17 – 7 December 1972

I-SPY Tick List:

• **Earthshine**	10	◯
• **Maria**	10	◯
• **Highlands**	10	◯

ARTIFICIAL SATELLITES

As you watch the sky, especially at dawn and dusk, you will often see a slow-moving point of light crossing the sky. This is an artificial **satellite**, orbiting the Earth. Some, such as Iridium satellites, become very bright and then fade away.

COMETS

You may be lucky enough to see a **comet**. Only rarely do these become bright enough for you to see them with the naked eye. A comet is a mixture of ice and dust – meteor dust comes from comets – and the heat of the Sun often makes it grow a long tail.

METEORS

Sometimes you see a sudden, short streak of light. This is often called a 'shooting star', but its proper name is a **meteor**. (They are not stars, but are tiny grains of dust that are burnt up as they dash through the Earth's atmosphere.) On a few nights of the year, the Earth passes through a cloud of dust, and we have a **meteor shower**, with dozens of meteors each hour. Very rarely, a meteor is brighter than any of the stars or planets; is then called a **fireball**.

Halley's Comet is the most famous. It returns every seventy-six years, most recently in 1986.

😊 I-SPY Tick List:

• **Satellite**	10	◯
• **Comet**	50	◯
• **Meteor**	10	◯
• **Meteor shower**	30	◯
• **Fireball**	50	◯

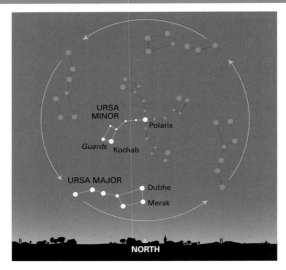

THE GREAT BEAR

It is best to start learning the sky
with the Plough (page 8). It forms
just part of the constellation
of **Ursa Major**, the Great Bear.
The picture shows how the
constellation used to be drawn
on old maps of the sky. The two
end stars are called the Pointers,
because a line through them
points to Polaris (page 8), the star
that stands still. The Pointers are
called **Dubhe** and **Merak**.

<table>
<tr><td colspan="3">😊 I-SPY Tick List:</td></tr>
<tr><td>• Ursa Major</td><td>10</td><td>◯</td></tr>
<tr><td>• Dubhe</td><td>10</td><td>◯</td></tr>
<tr><td>• Merak</td><td>10</td><td>◯</td></tr>
</table>

THE LITTLE BEAR

Polaris is the brightest star in **Ursa Minor**, the Little Bear (see page 22). The two stars closest to Ursa Major are known as **The Guards**, and one, **Kochab**, is quite bright. The diagram shown how the two constellations appear to swing round the North Pole (and Polaris) during the course of the night.

I-SPY Tick List:
- Ursa Minor   10 ◯
- The Guards   10 ◯
- Kochab   10 ◯

Why do the Great and Little Bear appear odd in all old constellation drawings?

10 points for the correct answer.

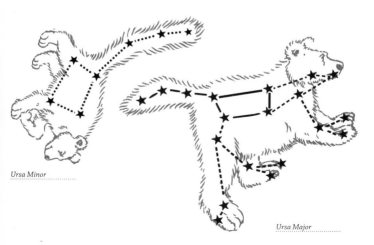

Ursa Minor

Ursa Major

CASSIOPEIA

There are several other constellations near the North Pole. If you find the star called **Megrez**, where Ursa Major's 'tail' joins the body, and imagine a line from there to Polaris and beyond, you come to a group of five stars in the shape of a 'W' or an 'M' when they are the other way up! These form the constellation of **Cassiopeia** (page 25), an ancient, legendary queen.

DRACO

Snaking its way around the pole is a long, faint constellation called **Draco**, the Dragon. At the end of its long, winding 'body', four stars make up its lozenge-shaped 'head'. The middle star of the three that form Ursa Major's 'tail' is Mizar. Between **Mizar** and the Guards is **Thuban** in Draco.

What is strange about Mizar (look at it through binoculars if you are not sure)?

10 points for the correct answer.

Cepheus

😊 I-SPY Tick List:	
• **Megrez**	10 〇
• **Cassiopeia**	10 〇
• **Draco**	10 〇
• **Mizar**	10 〇
• **Thuban**	10 〇
• **Cepheus**	10

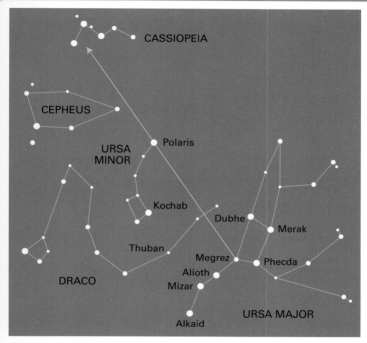

CEPHEUS

Between the head of Draco and
Cassiopeia is the constellation of
Cepheus (page 39), a legendary
king, husband of Cassiopeia. The
stars in this constellation form a
pointed shape like the gable end
of a house.

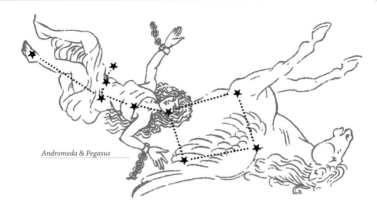

Andromeda & Pegasus

Do you know the Greek legend of how **Andromeda**, the daughter of Cassiopeia and Cepheus, came to be chained to a rock, and was about to be killed by the terrible sea-monster **Cetus** (see map page 48)?

She was rescued just in time by **Perseus**, who had earlier killed the dreadful Gorgon, Medusa. Medusa's head, with snakes for hair, turned anyone who looked at it to stone. (Perseus was clever and looked in a mirror.) He showed the head to Cetus, who became a rock.

After rescuing Andromeda, Perseus and Andromeda rode away on **Pegasus**, the flying horse (which appears upside-down in the sky).

You can find all these legendary beings in the sky (see the maps on pages 38 and 48, for example). The old constellation drawing of Perseus shows him holding Medusa's head. This is represented in the sky by the star **Algol**, whose name comes from the Arabic words Al Guhl, meaning 'the demon'. The photograph shows the constellation pattern and a bright comet, Comet Hyakutake.

Capella

η

γ

τ

α

δ

ε

ν

κ

φ

β Algol

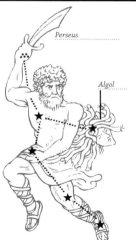

Perseus

Algol

I-SPY Tick List:

• **Cetus**	10	○
• **Perseus**	10	○
• **Pegasus**	10	○
• **Algol**	10	○

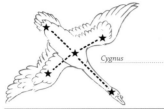

Cygnus

High in the sky in the middle of summer is the **Summer Triangle**, the corners of which are formed by the very bright stars of **Deneb** in **Cygnus**, the Swan; **Vega** in **Lyra**, the Lyre; and **Altair** in **Aquila**, the Eagle.

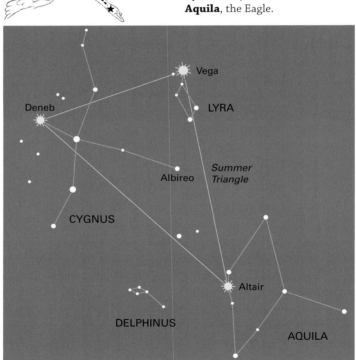

Summer Triangle

CYGNUS

Cygnus is sometimes known as the 'Northern Cross' and the name Deneb means 'the tail' in Arabic because it marks the tail of the Swan. The bright star at the other end (the 'beak') of the constellation is **Albireo**, but its name has no real meaning, because it arose after a series of errors and bad translations.

😊 I-SPY Tick List:

• **Summer Triangle**	10	◯
• **Deneb**	10	◯
• **Cygnus**	10	◯
• **Vega**	10	◯
• **Lyra**	10	◯
• **Altair**	10	◯
• **Aquila**	10	◯
• **Albireo**	10	◯

THE MILKY WAY

The Milky Way is a silvery band of light that stretches right across the sky and is easiest to see in summer. The faint light comes from hundreds of thousands of stars which are so closely crowded together that you cannot see them as individual stars.

With binoculars you can see that there appears no limit to the number of stars in the Milky Way, which is actually our edge-on view of the main disk of the Galaxy in which we live, and which contains over one hundred thousand million stars.

THE GREAT DARK RIFT

The densest part of the northern Milky Way runs from Cygnus down towards Sagittarius (page 45). Cygnus appears to be flying down the Milky Way. Can you see the **Great Dark Rift** in Cygnus? This may look like a 'hole in the stars', but actually there are just as many there as elsewhere in the Milky Way, but most are hidden by dark clouds of dust between the stars.

Milky Way

 Black holes are completely invisible, because not even light can escape from them, but they can be detected by their effects on nearby stars. The closest known black hole is orbiting a faint star in Cygnus.

🙂 I-SPY Tick List:

• **The Milky Way**	10	○
• **Great Dark Rift**	10	○

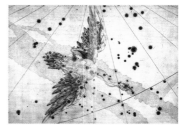

Cygnus

The Pleiades

OPEN CLUSTERS

Inside our own Galaxy stars are born in groups (known as clusters) from the material between the stars. Those with young, blue stars are known as open clusters, and usually contain a few tens of stars which are only a few million years old. The most famous open cluster is the **Pleiades**, in Taurus (see page 39). Other open clusters are older, such as the **Double Cluster** in Perseus (see map on page 42), which can be seen through binoculars.

GLOBULAR CLUSTERS

There are other clusters that are much older, at least ten thousand million years old. These are the globular clusters, which are spherical in shape and each contains many thousands of stars. The most famous in the northern sky is **M13, in Hercules** (see map page 50).

NEBULAE

A cloud of gas between the stars is known as a **nebula** (plural 'nebulae'), but only one, the great Orion Nebula (page 36) is easily visible to the naked eye.

I-SPY Tick List:

• Pleiades	10	◯
• Double Cluster	20	◯
• M13 in Hercules	10	◯
• Nebula	10	◯

Double Cluster

THE SEASONAL CHARTS

The charts on the following pages show the sky at four different seasons of the year. There are two charts for each season, one looking east, the other looking west.

AQUARIUS

PEGASUS

DELPHINUS

Altair

CYGNUS

CEPHEU

AQUILA

Albireo

Deneb

LYRA

Vega

HERCULES

DRACO

OPHIUCHUS

CORONA BOREALIS

Gemma

BOÖTES

Arcturus

Astronomers measure distances between the stars in light-years – the time it takes for light to travel from stars to us. Light travels at nearly 300,000 kilometres per second.

VIRGO

Spica

STARS AROUND THE NORTH POLE

This chart shows all the stars that you can see if you live in the Northern Hemisphere. With it you can find your way from one constellation to another. The North Pole of the sky and Polaris are in the centre.

Winter is the best time to see **Orion** and the stars of **Canis Major** and **Canis Minor**, the Greater and Lesser Dogs. **Betelgeuse**, in Orion, is a gigantic type of star, called a red supergiant. If it were in the Solar System in place of the Sun, the Earth would be below its surface. Its colour is in sharp contrast to bluish-white **Rigel** on the other side of the constellation. **Sirius**, in Canis Major, is the brightest star in the sky. Venus and Jupiter, which are planets (page 12), are the only objects that ever appear brighter.

What is another name for Sirius?

10 points for the correct answer.

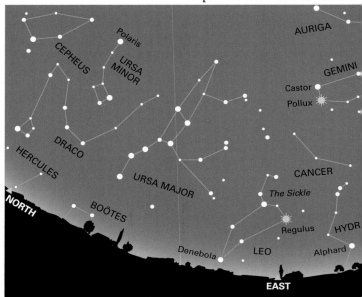

The Orion Nebula is a vast cloud of gas and dust, just visible to the naked eys as a fuzzy spot below Orion's belt. Dozens of new stars are being created within it.

Orion ....

😊 I-SPY Tick List:

- The stars of Orion's belt   10 ◯
- Canis Major   10 ◯
- Canis Minor   10 ◯
- Betelgeuse   10 ◯
- Rigel   10 ◯
- Sirius   10 ◯

Altair, one of the Summer Triangle (page 28) will have disappeared, but **Vega** can still be seen low on the horizon in the north-west, while **Deneb** is higher up in the same part of the sky. **Andromeda**, with its great galaxy (page 49) and the small neighbouring constellations of **Triangulum**, the Triangle, and **Aries**, the Ram, with one bright star, **Hamal**, are still easy to see.

High in the south is the constellation of **Perseus**, and lower down, **Taurus**, the Bull,

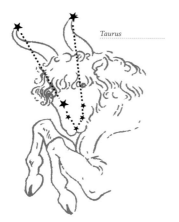

Taurus

whose 'eye' is orange **Aldebaran**. Taurus contains two clusters, the **Pleiades** (page 33) and the 'V' of stars near Aldebaran, known as the **Hyades**.

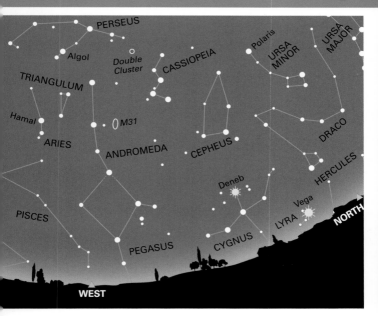

PERSEUS

Algol

Double
Cluster

CASSIOPEIA

Polaris

URSA
MINOR

URSA
MAJOR

TRIANGULUM

Hamal

ARIES

M31

ANDROMEDA

CEPHEUS

DRACO

HERCULES

PISCES

Deneb

Vega

LYRA

NORTH

PEGASUS

CYGNUS

WEST

I-SPY Tick List:	
• Triangulum	10 ◯
• Aries	10 ◯
• Hamal	10 ◯

I-SPY Tick List:	
• Taurus	10 ◯
• Aldebaran	10 ◯
• Hyades	10 ◯

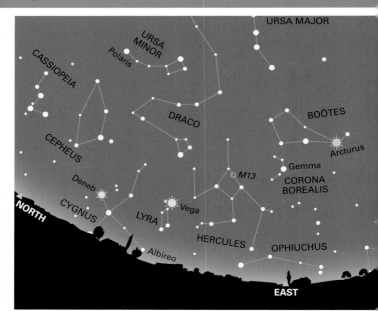

If you follow the line of the **Pointers**, not towards Polaris, but in the opposite direction, you come to the great constellation of **Leo**, the Lion. The 'backward question mark' of stars (with **Regulus** as the 'dot') forming the lion's head (see the next chart page 42) is known as **The Sickle**. At the other end of Leo, **Denebola** forms the 'tail' of the lion. You can follow the curve of the tail of Ursa Major, or a line from Regulus to Denebola, to help you find **Arcturus**, the brightest star in **Boötes**, the Herdsman. Low on the horizon are the four stars of **Corvus**, the Crow.

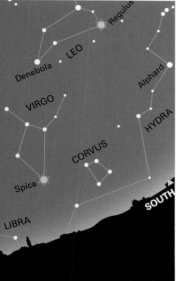

😊 I-SPY Tick List:

- Pointers 10 ◯
- Leo 10 ◯
- Regulus 10 ◯
- The Sickle 10 ◯
- Denebola 10 ◯
- Arcturus 10 ◯
- Boötes 10 ◯
- Corvus 10 ◯

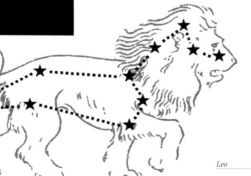

Leo

Spring is a good time to see the constellation of **Gemini**, the Twins, which consists of two, almost parallel lines of stars, running west from the two bright stars **Castor** and **Pollux**. Between Leo and Gemini is the faint constellation of **Cancer**, the Crab.

Below Gemini is the small constellation of **Canis Minor**, the Lesser Dog, with just one bright star, **Procyon**.

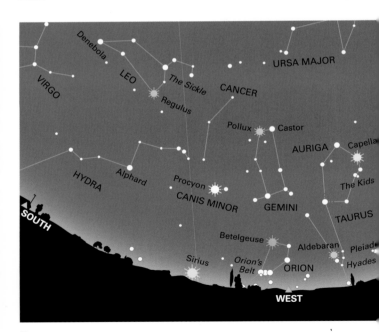

Spring – Looking West

High in the north-west is the constellation of **Auriga**, the Charioteer. In old drawings he is shown carrying two young goats in his arms, so the little triangle of stars to the right of bright **Capella** is known as **The Kids**.

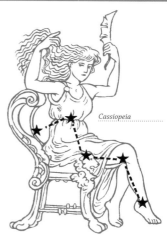

Cassiopeia

URSA MINOR
Polaris
DRACO
CASSIOPEIA
CEPHEUS
Double Cluster
Algol
ANDROMEDA
M31
PERSEUS
NORTH

😊 I-SPY Tick List:

• **Gemini**	10	◯
• **Castor**	10	◯
• **Pollux**	10	◯
• **Cancer**	10	◯
• **Procyon**	10	◯
• **Auriga**	10	◯
• **Capella**	10	◯
• **The Kids**	10	◯

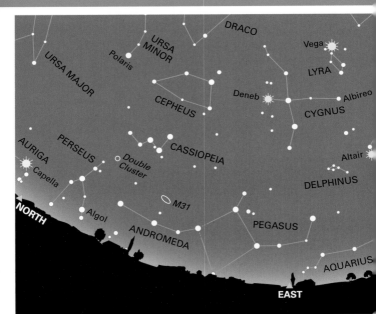

Although it does not get dark until very late and the nights are short, summer is the best time to see the great **Summer Triangle** (page 28) and the star clouds of the **Milky Way**, which consist of thousands and thousands of stars, too close together to be seen as separate points of light.

Very low in the south is **Sagittarius**, the Archer. Can you spy the **'Teapot'** among its stars? To the east is the fainter constellation of **Capricornus**, the Sea-Goat, and the rather brighter one of **Aquarius**, the Water Carrier. Between them and Cygnus lies the tiny constellation of **Delphinus**, the Dolphin.

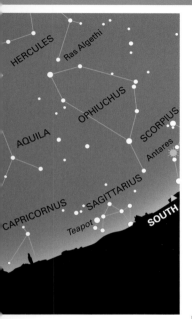

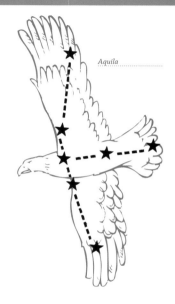

Aquila

😊 **I-SPY Tick List:**

• **Sagittarius**	10	◯
• **'Teapot'**	10	◯
• **Capricornus**	10	◯
• **Aquarius**	10	◯
• **Delphinus**	10	◯

I-SPY Summer – Looking West

If you follow the curve of the tail of the Plough (as described on page 41) and go beyond Arcturus, you come to **Spica**, the brightest star in the constellation of **Virgo**, the Virgin. East of Boötes is the semi-circle of stars of the constellation of **Corona Borealis**, the Northern Crown. The brightest star is called **Gemma**, the Jewel.

To the east lies the large constellation of **Ophiuchus**, the Serpent Bearer. Below this is **Scorpius**, the Scorpion. Its brightest star is **Antares**, the 'Rival of Mars', so called because, like the planet, it is deep red in colour. Between Antares and Spica lies the constellation of **Libra**, the Balance (or Scales).

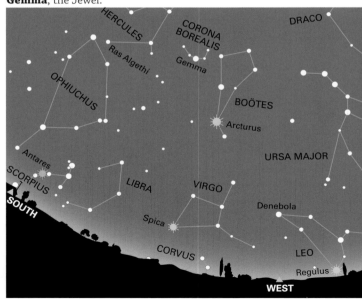

Milky Way

I-SPY Tick List:

• Spica	10	◯
• Virgo	10	◯
• Corona Borealis	10	◯
• Gemma	10	◯
• Ophiuchus	10	◯
• Scorpius	10	◯
• Antares	10	◯
• Libra	10	◯

Rising high in the east is the **Great Square of Pegasus**. The star at the north-eastern corner actually belongs to **Andromeda**. Part of the way along the line of four bright stars in Andromeda, two more point at right-angles to the north, indicating the position of the **Great Andromeda Galaxy** (also known as **M31**). It needs to be very clear and dark for you to see this galaxy. Just think, the light you see started its journey at about the time when the first humans began to evolve from ape-like creatures!

I-SPY Tick List:

• Great Square of Pegasus	10	◯
• Andromeda	10	◯
• The Great Andromeda Galaxy	10	◯
• Pisces	10	◯
• Cetus	10	◯
• Fomalhaut	10	◯

Below Pegasus lies the faint constellation of **Pisces**, the Fishes, and still farther south, there is the large area of sky known as **Cetus**, the Sea Monster. Unfortunately many of the stars in this area are rather faint. If you are lucky, however you may just be able to see, very, very low in the south, **Fomalhaut** in Piscis Austrinus, the Southern Fish.

Autumn – Looking East

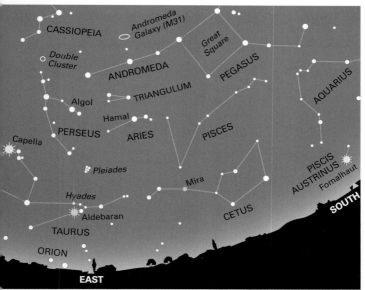

CASSIOPEIA

Andromeda Galaxy (M31)

Great Square

Double Cluster

ANDROMEDA

PEGASUS

TRIANGULUM

AQUARIUS

Algol

Hamal

PERSEUS

ARIES

PISCES

Capella

Pleiades

PISCIS AUSTRINUS

Mira

Fomalhaut

Hyades

SOUTH

Aldebaran

CETUS

TAURUS

ORION

EAST

M31

Like the constellations of Andromeda and Pegasus, **Hercules**, the legendary hero, is upside down! One foot rests on Draco in the north. The name of one star **Ras Algethi**, means 'the kneeling man's head' in Arabic. The main part of the body is known as the 'Keystone' because the arrangement of the four stars is just like the shape of the central stone in an archway. On the western side of the Keystone lies the globular **cluster, M13** (see page 23).

It is still possible to see most of the **Summer Triangle** and the bright stars of **Vega, Deneb** and **Altair** (see page 28) as well as much of the Milky Way which also runs through the constellations of Cassiopeia and Perseus.

How many labours did Hercules have to accomplish?

10 points for the correct answer.

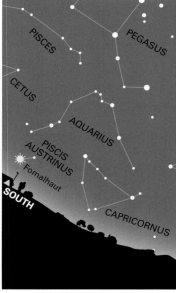

I-SPY Tick List:

• Hercules	10	○
• Ras Algethi	10	○
• The cluster M13	20	○

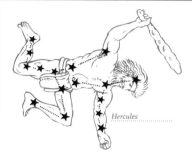

Hercules

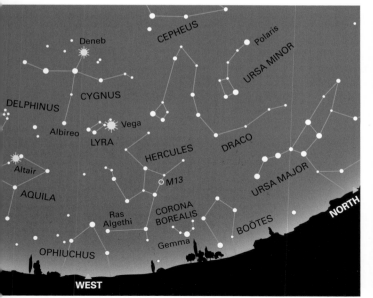

CEPHEUS

Polaris

URSA MINOR

Deneb

CYGNUS

DELPHINUS

Albireo   Vega

LYRA

HERCULES   DRACO

Altair

AQUILA

M13

URSA MAJOR

Ras
Algethi   CORONA
BOREALIS

BOÖTES

NORTH

OPHIUCHUS   Gemma

WEST

Sometimes, at Full Moon (page 16), the Earth comes between the Sun and the Moon and casts its shadow on the Moon, giving a lunar eclipse. (It does not always do this, because the Moon is sometimes above and sometimes below the line connecting the Earth and the Sun.) The Moon moves through the shadow from west to east, and you can watch the shadow creep across the Moon. The changes are easy to see with binoculars.

PARTIAL LUNAR ECLIPSES

Because of the variations in the Moon's position, frequently it does not pass through the centre of the Earth's shadow. Part of the Moon – usually the northern or southern region – remains sunlit, giving a **partial eclipse**.

😊 **I-SPY Tick List:**

• **Partial lunar eclipse**	10	◯
• **Total lunar eclipse**	20	◯
• **The colour of the moon**	10	◯

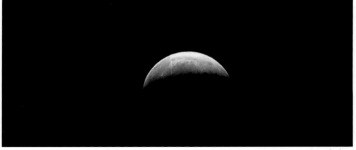

Partial eclipse

TOTAL LUNAR ECLIPSES

When the Moon does pass through the centre of the shadow, the whole surface is darkened in a **total eclipse**, which may last as long as 100 minutes. Very occasionally, if there are lots of clouds or large amounts of volcanic dust in the Earth's atmosphere, the Moon may appear very dark and almost disappear.

 It is thought that the Moon was created when a body, the size of Mars, hit the Earth with a glancing blow. Fragments formed a disk around the Earth and later combined into the Moon.

THE COLOUR OF THE MOON

Generally the Moon does not disappear completely at total eclipse. The Earth's atmosphere lets some red light through, so the Moon appears red. Usually there is enough light to make out the general shape of the dark maria (page 18), and sometimes even some prominent craters.

Although it does not happen at night, the Moon sometimes comes between the Sun and the Earth (at New Moon), similar to the way lunar eclipses occur. The Sun and Moon appear almost exactly the same size in the sky, and the Moon blocks out the sunlight to give a solar eclipse. This is a sight not to be missed if you have the chance.

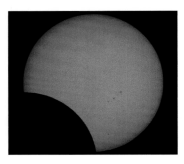

 You must NEVER look at the Sun through binoculars or a telescope, because it would damage your eyes or even blind you.

 I-SPY Tick List:

- **Partial solar eclipse 20** ◯
- **Total solar eclipse   50** ◯
- **Annular solar eclipse   40** ◯

PARTIAL SOLAR ECLIPSE

The Moon only throws a tiny shadow on the surface of the Earth, so you are much less likely to see a solar eclipse than a lunar one. You are most likely to see a **partial solar eclipse**, when the Moon hides just part of the Sun.

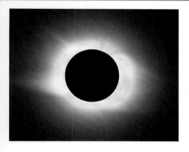

TOTAL SOLAR ECLIPSE

Along a very narrow line on the surface of the Earth, the Sun may be completely hidden by the Moon, in a **total solar eclipse**, generally for no more than about 3-4 minutes. The way the shadow sweeps across the Earth is very dramatic, and during totality the beautiful outer atmosphere of the Sun, the corona, becomes visible.

 It takes light about 8 minutes to reach us from the Sun, but about 4 years to travel to the nearest star (which is called Proxima Centauri).

ANNULAR SOLAR ECLIPSE

Because the distances to the Moon and Sun change, sometimes the Moon does not completely cover the disk of the Sun, and a ring of light remains visible, in an **annular eclipse**. Although only visible from a narrow path on the Earth, they can last for about 12 minutes, and are slightly more common than total eclipses.

NACREOUS CLOUDS

Rarely, shortly after sunset (or before sunrise, if you are up that early), you may see clouds with beautiful bands of different colours, These are **nacreous (mother-of-pearl) clouds** made of ice particles. They are so high (15-30 km) that they are illuminated by the Sun, even though the ground is in darkness.

😊 I-SPY Tick List:

• **Nacreous cloud**	30	◯
• **Noctilucent cloud**	30	◯
• **Aurora**	30	◯

NOCTILUCENT CLOUDS

Occasionally, during the summer months of late May, June and July, bluish-white, wispy clouds may be seen in the north, around midnight. These are **noctilucent ('night-shining') clouds**, the highest of all at about 80 km above the ground. They are also made of ice, and reflect light from the Sun that is hidden far below the northern horizon.

AURORA

Quite frequently, the Sun sends out streams of charged (that is, electrified) particles. When these hit the Earth's atmosphere, they cause the air to glow, giving an **aurora**: changing patterns of light high in the sky.

OBSERVATORY

You may be lucky enough to visit an observatory, which is where professional astronomers study the stars. They often have several telescopes, which are usually very large reflectors (page 6). Do not expect to look through one, though! The telescopes are only used with highly complicated digital cameras and other equipment. But many observatories have visitor centres that you can visit.

😀 I-SPY Tick List:

• **Observatory**	**10** ◯
• **Observatory visitor centre**	**10** ◯
• **A great telescope**	**10** ◯

Old Greenwich Observatory

I-SPY Tick List:

- Amateur observatory **10** ○
- Dome **10** ○
- Look through a telescope **20** ○

AMATEUR OBSERVATORY

Many local amateur astronomical societies have observatories, and these often hold open days where you can visit and may be able to look through some of the telescopes. Like professional observatories, the telescopes are usually protected by a **dome**.

12 and 4 inch telescope

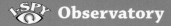
RADIO OBSERVATORY

Nowadays, astronomy is carried out in many different ways: with **radio telescopes** (with both large **dishes** and **'TV-type' aerials**), and with satellites. Again, some radio observatories have visitor centres, and you can see typical satellites at some **space centres**.

I-SPY Tick List:

• Radio Observatory	10	◯
• Radio Observatory visitor centre	20	◯
• Dish telescope	10	◯
• Radio telescope looking like many TV aerials	20	◯

Jodrell Bank Lovell telescope

Radio Telescope

Mullard Radio Observatory

You can learn a lot about astronomy by visiting a museum. Some are in old observatories. There you will often find displays explaining about planets, stars, galaxies, and other strange things like black holes! But you can also see many of the old instruments that earlier astonomers used.

CELESTIAL SPHERE

One of the simplest devices is a celestial sphere which shows the stars, usually with the old constellation drawings.

What is odd about a celestial globe?

10 points for the correct answer.

ASTROLABE

A more complicated device is an astrolabe, which is a special form of sky map. A planisphere (page 5) is a simplified modern version.

ORRERY

Sometimes you may see an orrery, which is a working model of the Solar System where the planets move at correct relative speeds around the Sun.

ARMILLARY SPHERE

You may also see an armillary sphere, with is a collection of rings that may be used to show the movements of the Sun, Moon and stars in the sky.

😊 I-SPY Tick List:

• Celestial sphere	10	◯
• Astrolabe	10	◯
• Armillary sphere	10	◯
• Orrery	10	◯
• Meteorite	10	◯

METEORITE

Occasionally some meteors (page 21) are large enough to land on Earth. You can find these meteorites in many museums. They are very old indeed, and tell scientists who study them about the time when the Sun and planets themselves were formed.